JERALD SIMON

MW00595708

Wintertide

instrumental piano solos

10 Original New Age/Contemporary Classical Piano Solos for Advanced Piano Students

MUSIC MENTOR

JERALD SIMON

MUSICMOTIVATION.COM

Cool music that excites, entertains, and educates!

visit **http://musicmotivation.com**
follow Jerald on Facebook: **https://facebook.com/jeraldsimon**
subscribe to Jerald's YouTube page: **https://youtube.com/jeraldsimon**

Music Motivation® books are designed to provide students with music instruction that will enable them to improve and increase their successes in the field of music. It is also intended to enhance appreciation and understanding of various styles of music from classical to jazz, blues, rock, popular, new age, hymns, and more. The author and publisher disclaim any liability or accountability for the misuse of this material as it was intended by the author.

Copyright © 2019 by **Music Motivation®** - All Rights Reserved - International Copyright Secured.
WARNING: The music, text, design, and graphics in this publication are protected by copyright law.
Any duplication in any form for any purpose is an infringement of U.S. copyright law.

I hope you enjoy "Wintertide". This book features 10 original new age/contemporary classical piano solos for advanced piano students.

I hope you enjoy playing these pieces. All of these original piano solos were composed to create a feeling of movement, change, and uplifting positivity.

Have fun with the music!

Your Music Mentor **Jerald Simon**

This book is dedicated to the many YouTube subscribers who watch my videos on my YouTube page (youtube.com/jeraldsimon) Also, for my wife, Suzanne (Zanny), my sweet daughter, Summer, and my two sons, Preston, and Matthew.

You can listen to the music from this book on Pandora, Spotify, iTunes, Amazon.com, and all streaming sites. It is also available for purchase as an MP3 album download or as a physical CD from Amazon.com or my website (musicmotivation.com).

The front and background image was taken by Jerald Simon

More best sellers by Jerald
Learn more about Jerald

CONNECT with Jerald

http://musicmotivation.com/jeraldsimon
https://facebook.com/jeraldsimon
http://youtube.com/jeraldsimon
http://linkedin.com/in/jeraldsimon
http://pinterest.com/jeraldsimon
https://twitter.com/jeraldsimon
http://cdbaby.com/artist/jeraldsimon
http://instagram.com/jeraldsimon
jeraldsimon@musicmotivation.com

CONTACT Music Motivation®

Music Motivation®
Cool music that excites, entertains, and educates!

Music Motivation®
P.O. Box 1000
Kaysville, UT 84037-1000
http://musicmotivation.com
https://facebook.com/musicmotivation
https://twitter.com/musicmotivation
info@musicmotivation.com

Copyright © 2019 by **Music Motivation®** All Rights Reserved - International Copyright Secured. No part of this book may be copied, reproduced, or duplicated in any form by any mechanical, electronic or other means known or hereafter invented without written permission from the author, Jerald Simon. For more promotional excerpt permission, contact Music Motivation®, **P.O. Box 1000 Kaysville, UT 84037-1000** - jeraldsimon@musicmotivation.com

First Printing 2019 - Printed in the United States of America - 10 9 8 7 6 5 4 3 2 1 - Simon, Jerald - Music Motivation® - Wintertide - $18.95 US/ $20.95 Canada - Soft cover spiral bound book - ISBN-13: 978-1-948274-10-4 , MM00001067

Music Motivation® is a registered ® trademark

Welcome to "*Wintertide*" by JERALD SIMON

In this book are 10 original new age/contemporary classical piano solos for advanced piano students. These pieces were composed to express the movement of wintertime across the piano keys. Most of the pieces range all over the piano keys in various key signatures.

You can listen to the music from this book on Pandora, Spotify, iTunes, Amazon.com, and all streaming sites. It is also available for purchase as an MP3 album download or as a physical CD from Amazon.com or from my website (musicmotivation.com). Follow me on any of these music stations and follow my daily 5 minute YouTube piano lessons on my YouTube channel: **youtube.com/jeraldsimon.**

"My purpose and mission in life is to motivate myself and others through my music and writing, to help others find their purpose and mission in life, and to teach values that encourage everyone everywhere to do and be their best." - Jerald Simon

A message from Jerald to piano students and parents:

If you come to piano lessons each week and walk away only having learned about music notation, rhythm, and dots on a page, then I have failed as a Music Mentor. Life lessons are just as important, if not more important than music lessons. I would rather have you learn more about goal setting and achieving, character, dedication, and personal improvement. To have you learn to love music, appreciate it, and play it, is a wonderful byproduct you will have for the rest of your life - a talent that will enrich your life and the lives of others. To become a better musician is wonderful and important, but to become a better person is more important.

As a Music Mentor I want to mentor students to be the very best they can be. If you choose not to practice, you essentially choose not to improve. This is true in any area of life. Everyone has the same amount of time allotted to them. What you choose to do with your time, and where you spend your time, has little to do with the activities being done and more to do with the value attached to each activity.

I believe it's important to be well-rounded and have many diverse interests. I want students to enjoy music, to learn to be creative and understand how to express themselves musically - either by creating music of their own, or interpreting the music of others - by arranging and improvising well known music. In addition, I encourage students to play sports, dance, sing, draw, read, and develop all of their talents. I want them to be more than musicians, I want them to learn to become well-rounded individuals.

Above all, I want everyone to continually improve and do their best. I encourage everyone to set goals, dream big, and be the best they can be in whatever they choose to do. Life is full of wonderful choices. Choose the best out of life and learn as much as you can from everyone everywhere. I prefer being called a Music Mentor because I want to mentor others and help them to live their dreams.

Your life is your musical symphony. Make it a masterpiece!

JERALD SIMON

Copyright © 2019 by Music Motivation® - http://musicmotivation.com

Many piano teachers, piano students, and parents of piano students ask me how or why I began creating the "Cool Songs" from my **"Cool Songs Subscription"** (musicmotivation.com/coolsongs). It began with my "Cool Songs for Cool Kids" Series (Primer Level and Books 1, 2, and 3), and my "Cool Songs that ROCK!" Series (books 1 and 2). To be honest, however, it actually began long before any of those books were created.

I began teaching piano lessons part time in 2003, I was newly married and was selling pianos in a piano store. I didn't start teaching full time as an independent piano teacher until 2006. Between 2003 and 2006 I had a few different sales jobs I did as well, while continuing to do things on the side for my music career. In 2006 I created my music company, **Music Motivation®**, at first for my piano studio and for me as a performing musician. I then felt motivated to come out with two books back to back. The first book I ever created was "An Introduction to Scales and Modes". It is an in-depth tutorial of basic scales and modes in all key signatures. After that I came out with my second book, "Variations on Mary Had a Little Lamb." This book has nine different arrangements I created using the children's song, "Mary Had a Little Lamb." These are some of the arrangements in the book: Mary Took Her Lamb to a Swingin' Jazz Club, Mary's Lamb Had the Blues, Mary Took Her Lamb to a 50s Rock Concert, Mary and Her Lamb Live with Indians, etc., etc., until the last arrangement of: Mary Took Her Lamb to a Funeral.

These books were created to help students learn the theory and the practical application of the music. As a result of these two books, my piano studio more than doubled. At my most busy time in teaching, I had around 88 piano students. The majority were teenage boys (ages 11-19), and most of them wanted to quit piano lessons. Piano teachers and parents of piano students would send me their students who essentially wanted nothing more to do with the instrument. The parents and teachers said they didn't want their students to quit and asked me to try to motivate them to keep playing the piano (I guess that is what I get for naming my company Music Motivation®). The students would not play from any method book past or present and would never suggest music they wanted to play. I needed to figure out how to reach these students and connect with them. I asked each of them what kind of music they enjoyed and asked them to bring it so they could work on it. The majority would not do it. I then asked them to challenge me to create or compose a piano solo for them during their lesson. They all found this very entertaining. I would tell them to choose a style of music, key signature, and the time signature. With some pieces, such as "Game Over" from "Cool Songs for Cool Kids" book 1, they even said I could only use four notes. It was a game for the students and a challenge for me. With each of these students, I composed a piano solo during their lesson time and even notated it in Finale. At the end of their lesson I printed off the music and sent it home with them. I challenged them to learn the piano solo and then let me know what they thought. I told them I would compose a new piece the following week during their next lesson for them.

It worked! The following week, the students returned and I asked them if they had tried to play it. The majority of these students had not only tried to play it, but had perfected the piece and said they were ready to challenge me to compose a new piano solo. I would accept their challenge and tell them they would need to play what I composed. I asked the students what they honestly thought about the music and almost without exception, the students said they thought the music sounded "cool." They told me they would play the piano more if they could have more "cool" sounding music like the piano solo I had composed. I appreciated their positive feedback. I told them I would emphasize the music theory in the "cool song" because they need to know their music theory, but I also told them I wanted them to have fun learning these "cool songs" each week. That is how it all began. All of the "cool songs" I had composed in each lesson were later compiled into "Cool Songs for Cool Kids" books 1, 2, and 3. Because of the great feedback of these books, I then created "Cool Songs that ROCK!" books 1 and 2 for older teenagers that were a little more advanced. I have my students play through all of the "cool songs" I create so I can receive their feedback . They know what they like and what sounds "cool" to them. I listen to and now receive feedback from many piano teachers, piano students, and parents of piano students around the world who tell me what they would like me to compose as well. Have fun with this music!

- JERALD

Copyright © 2019 by Music Motivation® - http://musicmotivation.com

	♪ Apprentice ♪ for 1st & 2nd year students	♪ Maestro ♪ for 2nd - 4th year students	♪ Virtuoso ♪ for 3rd year students and above
Repertoire *In addition to the books listed to the right, students can sign up to receive the weekly "Cool Song" and "Cool Exercise" composed by Jerald Simon every week. Visit musicmotivation.com/annualsubscription to learn more and sign up!*	**Music Motivation® Book(s)** What Every Pianist Should Know (Free PDF) Essential Piano Exercises (section 1) Cool Songs for Cool Kids (pre-primer level) Cool Songs for Cool Kids (primer level) Cool Songs for Cool Kids (book 1) The Pentascale Pop Star (books 1 and 2) Songs in Pentascale position: Classical, Jazz, Blues, Popular, Students Choice, Personal Composition (in pentascale position - 5 note piano solo) etc.	**Music Motivation® Book(s)** Essential Piano Exercises (section 2) An Introduction to Scales and Modes Cool Songs for Cool Kids (book 2) Cool Songs for Cool Kids (book 3) Variations on Mary Had a Little Lamb Twinkle Those Stars, Jazzed about Christmas, Jazzed about 4th of July Baroque, Romantic, Classical, Jazz, Blues, Popular, New Age, Student's Choice, Personal Composition.	**Music Motivation® Book(s)** Essential Piano Exercises (section 3) Cool Songs that ROCK! (books 1 & 2) Triumphant, Sea Fever, Sweet Melancholy, The Dawn of a New Age, Sweet Modality, Jazzed about Jazz, Jazzed about Classical Music, Jingle Those Bells, Cinematic Solos, Hymn Arranging Baroque, Romantic, Classical, Jazz, Blues, Popular, New Age, Contemporary, Broadway Show Tunes, Standards, Student's Choice, Personal Composition
Music Terminology	Piano (*p*), Forte (*f*) Mezzo Piano (*mp*) Mezzo Forte (*mf*) Pianissimo (*pp*) Fortissimo (*ff*) *Music Motivation® 1st Year Terminology*	Tempo Markings Dynamic Markings Parts of the Piano Styles and Genres of Music *Music Motivation® 2nd Year Terminology*	Pocket Music Dictionary (2 - 3 years) Harvard Dictionary of Music (4 + years) Parts/History of the Piano Music Composers (Weekly Biographies) *Music Motivation® 3rd Year Terminology*
Key Signatures	C, G, D, A, F, B♭, E♭ & A♭ (Major) A, E, B, F♯, D, G, C & F (Minor) Begin learning all major key signatures	Circle of 5ths/Circle of 4ths All Major and Minor key signatures (Identify each key and name the sharps and flats)	Spiral of Fifths, Chord Progressions within Key Signatures. Modulating from one Key Signature to another.
Music Notation	Names and Positions of notes on the staff (both hands - Treble and Bass Clefs)	Names and Positions of notes above and below the staff (both hands)	History of Music Notation (the development of notation), Monks & Music, Gregorian Chants, Music changes over the years and how music has changed. Learn Finale and Logic Pro (notate your music)
Rhythms	Whole notes/rests (say it and play it - count out loud) Half notes/rests (say it and play it - count out loud) Quarter notes/rests (say it and play it - count out loud) Eighth notes/rests (say it and play it - count out loud)	Sixteenth notes/rests (say it and play it - count out loud) Thirty-second notes/rests (say it and play it - count out loud) Sixty-fourth notes/rests (say it and play it - count out loud)	One-hundred-twenty-eighth notes/rests For more on rhythm, I recommend: "Rhythmic Training" by Robert Starer and "Logical Approach to Rhythmic Notation" (books 1 & 2) by Phil Perkins
Intervals	1st, 2nd, 3rd, 4th, 5th, 6th, 7th, 8th, and 9th intervals (key of C, G, D, F, B♭, and E♭). Harmonic and Melodic intervals (key of C, G, D, A, E, and B)	All Perfect, Major, Minor, Augmented, and Diminished intervals (in every key) All Harmonic and Melodic intervals Explain the intervals used to create major, minor, diminished, and augmented chords?	9th, 11th, and 13th intervals Analyze music (Hymns and Classical) to identify intervals used in each measure. Identify/Name intervals used in chords.
Scales	All Major Pentascales (5 finger scale) All Minor Pentascales (5 finger scale) All Diminished Pentascales (5 finger scale) C Major Scale (1 octave) A min. Scale (1 oct.) (Do, Re, Mi, Fa, Sol, La, Ti, Do) (solfege) All Major and Natural Minor Scales - 1 octave	All Major Scales (Every Key 1 - 2 octaves) All Minor Scales (Every Key 1 - 2 octaves) (natural, harmonic, and melodic minor scales) (Do, Di, Re, Ri, Mi, Fa, Fi, Sol, Si, La, Li, Ti, Do) (solfege - chromatic)	All Major Scales (Every Key 3 - 5 Octaves) All Minor Scales (Every Key 3 - 5 Octaves) All Blues Scales (major and minor) Cultural Scales (25 + scales)
Modes	Ionian/Aeolian (C/A, G/E, D/B, A/F♯)	All Modes (I, D, P, L, M, A, L) All keys	Modulating with the Modes (Dorian to Dorian)
Chords	All Major Chords, All Minor Chords, All Diminished Chords, C Sus 2, C Sus 4, C+ (Aug.), C 6th, C minor 6th, C 7th, C Maj. 7th, C minor Major 7th, A min., A Sus 2, A Sus 4,	All Major, Minor, Diminished, Augmented, Sus 2, Sus 4, Sixth, Minor Sixth, Dominant 7th and Major 7th Chords	Review All Chords from 1st and 2nd year experiences All 7th, 9th, 11th, and 13th chords inversions and voicings.
Arpeggios	Same chords as above (1 - 2 octaves)	Same chords as above (3 - 4 octaves)	Same chords as above (4 + octaves)
Inversions	Same chords as above (1 - 2 octaves)	Same chords as above (3 - 4 octaves)	Same chords as above (4 + octaves)
Technique (other)	Schmitt Preparatory Exercises, (Hanon)	Wieck, Hanon, Bach (well tempered clavier)	Bertini-Germer, Czerny, I. Philipp
Sight Reading	Key of C Major and G Major	Key of C, G, D, A, E, F, B♭, E♭, A♭, D♭	All Key Signatures, Hymns, Classical
Ear Training	Major versus Minor sounds (chords/intervals)	C, D, E, F, G, A, B, and intervals	Key Signatures and Chords, Play w/ IPod
Music History	The origins of the Piano Forte	Baroque, Classical, Jazz, Blues	Students choice - All genres, Composers
Improvisation	Mary Had a Little Lamb, Twinkle, Twinkle...	Blues Pentascale, Barrelhouse Blues	Classical, New Age, Jazz, Blues, etc. Play w/ IPod
Composition	5 note melody (both hands - key of C and G)	One - Two Page Song (include key change)	Lyrical, Classical, New Age, Jazz, etc.

This is only an outline or suggestion - add to it or subtract from it! If you are doing something different all together that works, keep doing it. This is meant to give you ideas and supplement what you're already doing.

The books from the Music Motivation® Series by Jerald Simon are not method books, and are not intentionally created to be used as such (although some piano teachers use them as such). Jerald simply creates fun, cool piano music to motivate piano students to play the piano and teach them music theory - the FUN way!

A few theory FUNdamentals to work on! (Practice these)

Here are a few exercises to warm up with before playing the pieces in this book. The majority of the pieces feature octave intervals (blocked or broken) with the left hand and various left hand patterns created from using the various notes from the scale of the given key signature (1 -5 - 8 - 9 - 10 or C - G - C - D - E as an example).

Start off playing all of the octave intervals (blocked - two notes played together at the same time) below. These exercises have been written moving up in half steps through every key signature (chromatically).

Now play all major octave intervals (broken - one note played after the other) moving up in half steps.

Copyright © 2019 by Music Motivation® - http://musicmotivation.com

MM00001067

A few theory FUNdamentals to work on! (Practice these)

Now play all major octave chords moving up in half steps. These octave chords are simply the basic triad (i.e. C E G) combined with an octave interval (i.e. C and C). Together they make the octave chords.

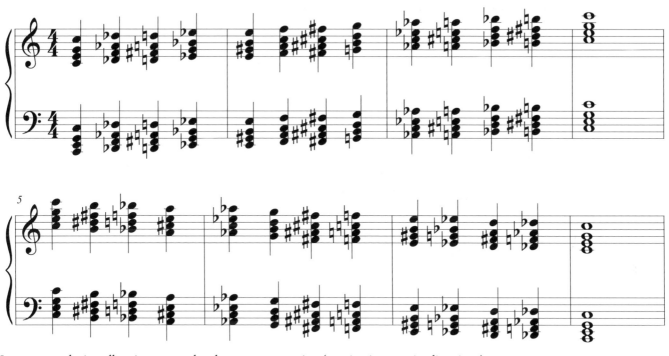

Now you are playing all major octave chords - contrary motion (moving in opposite directions).

Try playing all of these octave chords in every inversion (root position, 1st, 2nd, and 3rd inversions - in all keys moving up in half steps). You can try playing these exercises blocked, broken, left hand then right hand or right hand then left hand, outside notes then inside notes, or inside notes then outside notes, and many other ways. One of the best exercises you can do is playing your scales and chords in all key signatures. If you can play something in one key signature, you should be able to play it in all key signatures. This includes scales, chords, exercises, and even musical pieces.

Copyright © 2019 by Music Motivation® - http://musicmotivation.com

Below I have included all major octave chords moving in contrary motion (opposite directions from each other).

This exercise and the previous exercises are great warm ups you should do every day before you play the piano!

8

Copyright © 2019 by Music Motivation® - http://musicmotivation.com

MM00001067

Wintertide

by Jerald Simon

Copyright © 2019 by Music Motivation® - http://musicmotivation.com
All Rights Controlled and Administered by ASCAP
International Copyright Secured
All rights reserved including the right of public performance for profit

MM00001067

Copyright © 2019 by Music Motivation® - http://musicmotivation.com

MM00001067

MM00001067

Copyright © 2019 by Music Motivation® - http://musicmotivation.com

Copyright © 2019 by Music Motivation® - http://musicmotivation.com

MM00001067

MM00001067

Copyright © 2019 by Music Motivation® - http://musicmotivation.com

Copyright © 2019 by Music Motivation® - http://musicmotivation.com

MM00001067

MM00001067

Copyright © 2019 by Music Motivation® - http://musicmotivation.com

Copyright © 2019 by Music Motivation® - http://musicmotivation.com

MM00001067

MM00001067

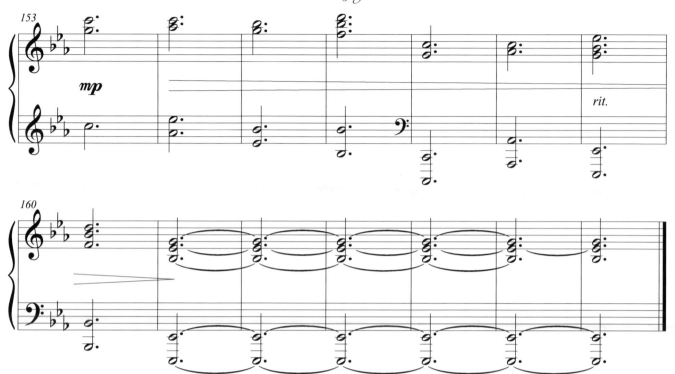

Copyright © 2019 by Music Motivation® - http://musicmotivation.com

MM0000106

Clarity

by JERALD SIMON

Copyright © 2019 by Music Motivation® - http://musicmotivation.com
All Rights Controlled and Administered by ASCAP
International Copyright Secured
All rights reserved including the right of public performance for profit

MM00001067

Copyright © 2019 by Music Motivation® - http://musicmotivation.com

MM0000106

Copyright © 2019 by Music Motivation® - http://musicmotivation.com

Copyright © 2019 by Music Motivation® - http://musicmotivation.com

MM00001067

Copyright © 2019 by Music Motivation® - http://musicmotivation.com

Copyright © 2019 by Music Motivation® - http://musicmotivation.com

MM00001067

MM00001067

Copyright © 2019 by Music Motivation® - http://musicmotivation.com

MM00001067

Copyright © 2019 by Music Motivation® - http://musicmotivation.com

Cloud Nine

Mysteriously ♩ = 65

by JERALD SIMON

pedal ad-lib throughout

Copyright © 2019 by Music Motivation® - http://musicmotivation.com
All Rights Controlled and Administered by ASCAP
International Copyright Secured
All rights reserved including the right of public performance for profit

28

Copyright © 2019 by Music Motivation® - http://musicmotivation.com

Copyright © 2019 by Music Motivation® - http://musicmotivation.com

MM0000106'

Copyright © 2019 by Music Motivation® - http://musicmotivation.com

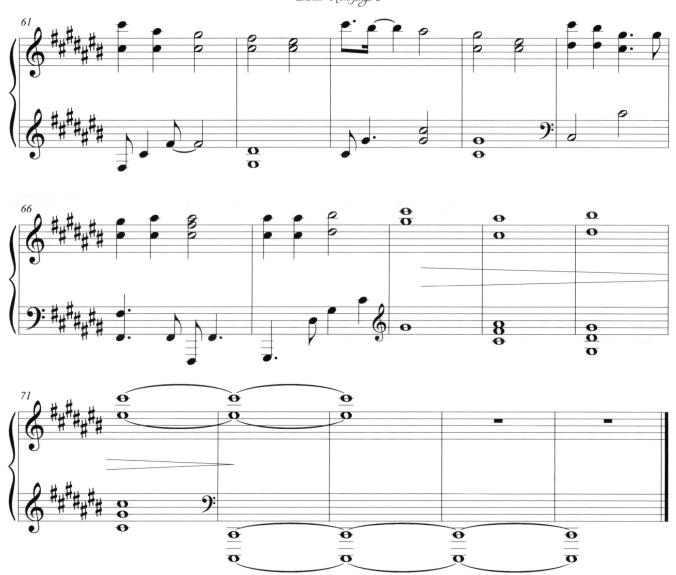

Copyright © 2019 by Music Motivation® - http://musicmotivation.com

MM00001067

Heaven's Vault

by JERALD SIMON

Copyright © 2019 by Music Motivation® - http://musicmotivation.com
All Rights Controlled and Administered by ASCAP
International Copyright Secured
All rights reserved including the right of public performance for profit

MM00001067

Copyright © 2019 by Music Motivation® - http://musicmotivation.com

MM00001067

MM00001067

Copyright © 2019 by Music Motivation® - http://musicmotivation.com

MM00001067

Copyright © 2019 by Music Motivation® - http://musicmotivation.com

Copyright © 2019 by Music Motivation® - http://musicmotivation.com

MM0000106

MM00001067

Copyright © 2019 by Music Motivation® - http://musicmotivation.com

MM00001067

Copyright © 2019 by Music Motivation® - http://musicmotivation.com

Copyright © 2019 by Music Motivation® - http://musicmotivation.com

MM00001067

MM00001067

Copyright © 2019 by Music Motivation® - http://musicmotivation.com

MM00001067

Copyright © 2019 by Music Motivation® - http://musicmotivation.com

48   Copyright © 2019 by Music Motivation® - http://musicmotivation.com   MM00001067

Copyright © 2019 by Music Motivation® - http://musicmotivation.com

Copyright © 2019 by Music Motivation® - http://musicmotivation.com

MM00001067

Copyright © 2019 by Music Motivation® - http://musicmotivation.com

Eden's Gate

Moving - Filled with Emotion ♩ = 60

by JERALD SIMON

pedal ad-lib throughout

Copyright © 2019 by Music Motivation® - http://musicmotivation.com
All Rights Controlled and Administered by ASCAP
International Copyright Secured
All rights reserved including the right of public performance for profit

MM00001067

MM00001067

Copyright © 2019 by Music Motivation® - http://musicmotivation.com

Copyright © 2019 by Music Motivation® - http://musicmotivation.com

MM00001067

Arcadia

by JERALD SIMON

Copyright © 2019 by Music Motivation® - http://musicmotivation.com
All Rights Controlled and Administered by ASCAP
International Copyright Secured
All rights reserved including the right of public performance for profit

MM00001067

55

Copyright © 2019 by Music Motivation® - http://musicmotivation.com

MM0000106

MM00001067

Copyright © 2019 by Music Motivation® - http://musicmotivation.com

MM0000106

Azure Sky

With Purpose ♩ = 60

by JERALD SIMON

Copyright © 2019 by Music Motivation® - http://musicmotivation.com
All Rights Controlled and Administered by ASCAP
International Copyright Secured
All rights reserved including the right of public performance for profit

MM00001067

Copyright © 2019 by Music Motivation® - http://musicmotivation.com

MM00001067

Copyright © 2019 by Music Motivation® - http://musicmotivation.com

Copyright © 2019 by Music Motivation® - http://musicmotivation.com

MM00001067

Copyright © 2019 by Music Motivation® - http://musicmotivation.com

Afterworld

by Jerald Simon

Copyright © 2019 by Music Motivation® - http://musicmotivation.com
All Rights Controlled and Administered by ASCAP
International Copyright Secured
All rights reserved including the right of public performance for profit

MM00001067

MM00001067

Copyright © 2019 by Music Motivation® - http://musicmotivation.com

65

Copyright © 2019 by Music Motivation® - http://musicmotivation.com

MM00001067

Copyright © 2019 by Music Motivation® - http://musicmotivation.com

Copyright © 2019 by Music Motivation® - http://musicmotivation.com

MM00001067

Copyright © 2019 by Music Motivation® - http://musicmotivation.com

Kingdom Come

by JERALD SIMON

Expressively ♩ = 70

pedal ad-lib throughout

cresc.

Copyright © 2019 by Music Motivation® - http://musicmotivation.com
All Rights Controlled and Administered by ASCAP
International Copyright Secured
All rights reserved including the right of public performance for profit

MM00001067

MM00001067

Copyright © 2019 by Music Motivation® - http://musicmotivation.com

Copyright © 2019 by Music Motivation® - http://musicmotivation.com

MM00001067

MM00001067

Copyright © 2019 by Music Motivation® - http://musicmotivation.com

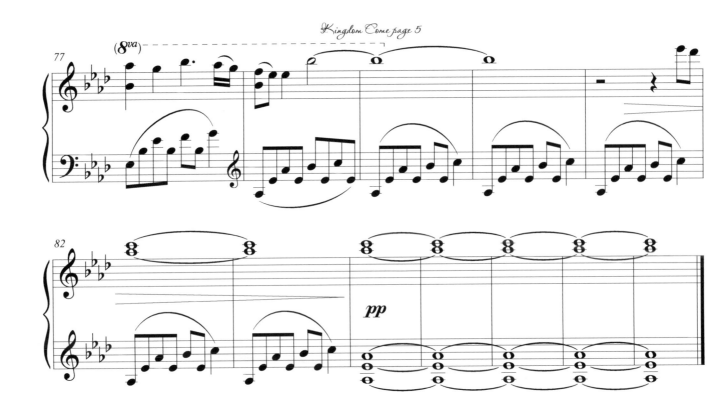

74   Copyright © 2019 by Music Motivation® - http://musicmotivation.com   MM0000106

Testimonials about Jerald

here are a few testimonials from musicians and piano teachers

"Jerald's hymn arrangements are as beautiful as they are musically interesting. I'm sure people are going to love hearing them in church meetings or wherever they are played."

- Jon Schmidt - Piano Guys

"Jerald is a wonderful human being who has inspired not only me to be a better pianist, but hundreds of other people. Keep up all the great work Jerald."

- Paul Cardall - Music Producer, Film Composer, Recording Artist

"What I love about arrangements of well-sung songs done by various artists is that one can hear the pianist's personality come through in a very real and intimate way. Jerald's passion for life and his beliefs comes through in his unique and distinctive arrangements of these well-known religious hymns."

- Kurt Bestor (Owner, Kurt Bestor Music)

"Jerald Simon's arrangement of A Poor Wayfaring Man of Grief is peaceful and soothing. It is not rushed, allowing lines to breathe and resolve. He continues to produce music that will bring spiritual comfort to those who are listening."

- Josh Wright (concert pianist and online piano teacher)

"Jerald Simon is a brilliant musician, teacher, and performer, with a fascinating story to tell. If you're interested in learning how to improvise or compose music, be sure to check out his books."

- Brandon Pearce - Owner, Music Teacher's Helper, LLC

"Jerald's motivational poetry, writing and music education books are a true expression of Jerald's winning personality and innovation. He is a Utah treasure."

- David Burger, Music critic, arts reporter, Salt Lake Tribune

"Not only do you get a song per week to learn, but all of the "fixings" (supplements) to go with it! Backing tracks, PDFs and also a step by step video going though each song. Wow! It's a great value for the price. I think students would enjoy playing these (cool) songs. Teachers and students shouldn't think twice about learning about (Jerald's) compositions and letting themselves be inspired by his musical style. Don't delay - jump in today!"

- Jeff Willie - Piano Teacher

"My favorite thing about the "Cool Songs" is the music theory that is introduced in the YouTube videos. So many times, students don't understand the why behind theory until they have been taking lessons for several years. The videos introduce theory concepts in a way that compliments the song, and then gives students a reason to actually use it!" Thanks again!

-Amanda W Smith (Piano Teacher - Founder of modernmusicteaching.com

youtube.com/jeraldsimon

On my YouTube channel, **youtube.com/jeraldsimon**, I have a few different playlists filled with great content for beginning piano students up to advanced piano students. The videos are geared for everyone from brand new piano students to music majors, professional pianists, and piano teachers of all skill levels.

There are three main playlists for my **free online piano lessons.** I offer in person piano lessons, skype/FaceTime piano lessons, and step by step piano lesson packages you can purchase and watch at home, but the ones listed below are FREE to everyone who subscribes to my YouTube channel:

1. **PIANO FUNdamentals** (emphasis on the word FUN!)

2. **5 Minute Piano Lessons with Jerald Simon**
(sponsored by Music Motivation)

3. **Theory Tip Tuesday Piano Lessons**

I frequently release new videos. Some are piano lessons, and others are filmings of workshops, masterclasses, or concerts. I also have these additional types of videos on my YouTube channel:

a. Meditation/Relaxation Music Composed by Jerald Simon
b. Hymn Arrangements by Jerald Simon
c. Motivational Messages by Jerald Simon
d. Motivational Poetry by Jerald Simon
e. Theory Tip Tuesday (FREE Weekly Piano Lesson Videos) by Jerald Simon
f. Cool Songs by Jerald Simon (musicmotivation.com/coolsongs)
g. Assemblies, Workshops, Firesides, and more...

Let me know if you have a tutorial you'd like me to come out with to better help you learn the piano. I'm happy to help in any way I can and love hearing feedback from others about what they personally are looking for in piano lesson videos to help them learn to play the piano better. I primarily focus on music theory, improvisation/arranging, and composition. I refer to these as THEORY THERAPY, INNOVATIVE IMPROVISATION, and CREATIVE COMPOSITION.

I have also produced hundreds of COOL SONGS that teach students music theory the fun way. You can choose one of five COOL SONGS packages on my website. If you'd like to learn more about the COOL SONGS (as I call them), that I composed to motivate my own piano students, or if you would like to purchase any of the COOL SONGS packages featuring the music/books, simply visit musicmotivation.com/coolsongs to be taken to the page on my website that explains a little more about the COOL SONGS. You can also watch piano video tutorial lessons featuring 85 of the 200 + COOL SONGS (youtube.com/jeraldsimon). Let me know what you think. I'd love your feedback about the music. It helps me as I compose more COOL SONGS to motivate more piano students. I'm excited to have you watch my free video piano lessons on YouTube.com/jeraldsimon.

Copyright © 2019 by Music Motivation® - http://musicmotivation.com

Perceptions, Parables, and Pointers by JERALD SIMON (read more at this link): http://musicmotivation.com/shop/motivationalself-help-books/perceptions-parables-and-pointers-by-jerald-simon/

What do you really want to do with your time? What is your mission in life? Where have you been, and where would you like to go? What are your dreams, your hopes, your wishes? If you could do anything in the world, what would it be?

The main goal in writing down these perceptions, parables, and pointers, and in creating this book in general, is to present ideas that will help get people thinking, imagining, planning, creating, and actively participating in life.

The "As If" Principle (motivational poetry) by JERALD SIMON features 222 original motivational poems written by Simon to inspire and motivate men, women, businesses, organizations, leaders, mentors, advisers, teachers, and students. The poems were written to teach values and encourage everyone everywhere to do and be their best. (read more at this link): http://musicmotivation.com/shop/motivationalself-help-books/the-as-if-principle-by-jerald-simon/

CHECK OUT
JERALD'S
MOTIVATIONAL
BOOKS

PERCEPTIONS,
PARABLES,
AND
POINTERS
$19.95

216 PAGES

A SELF-HELP
MOTIVATION
MANUAL

MOTIVATION IN A MINUTE
$18.95

FULL COLOR PICTURES
AND MOTIVATIONAL MESSAGES

THE "AS IF"
PRINCIPLE
(MOTIVATIONAL
POETRY)
$16.95

154 PAGES

222 INSPIRATIONAL
AND MOTIVATIONAL
POEMS WRITTEN
BY JERALD

ALL BOOKS ARE AVAILABLE ON AMAZON, BARNES AND NOBLE,
AND ALL ONLINE AND TRADITIONAL BOOK STORES

Copyright © 2019 by Music Motivation® - http://musicmotivation.com

Jerald's Albums & Singles
are available from all online music stores

Stream Jerald's music on
Pandora, Spotify, iTunes, Amazon, and all streaming sites.

Music Books, Albums, MP3s, Self Help and Motivational Books, Poetry Books and YouTube Videos
Check out my books and music on **iTunes, Amazon, Spotify, Pandora, & YouTube.com/jeraldsimon**
Motivate Piano Students! Music Motivation® - P.O. Box 1000 - Kaysville, UT 84037-1000

Check out Jerald's Cool Song Piano Packages

Jerald continually produces and releases new "Cool Songs" available for all piano students and piano teachers on his website (*musicmotivation.com*). Each new *"Cool Song"* is emailed to Music Motivation® mentees (piano teachers and piano students) who have enrolled in the "COOL SONGS" monthly subscription program. See which subscription is the best fit for you and for your piano students (if you are a piano teacher) by visiting:

http://musicmotivation.com/coolsongs

At **Music Motivation**®, I strive to produce the best quality products I can to help musicians of all ages better understand music theory (Theory Therapy), improvisation (Innovative Improvisation), and composition (Creative Composition). I try to tailor my products around the needs of piano teachers and piano students of all ages - from beginning through advanced and would love to receive your feedback about what I can do to better help you teach and learn. Let me know if there is a type of piano music, music book, fun audio or video tutorial, or any other educational product you would like to see in the field of music (principally the piano), but have not yet found, that would help you teach and learn the piano better. Please contact me. I look forward to your comments and suggestions. Thank you.

Check out these best sellers by Jerald Simon

Jerald is continually coming out with new books and has multiple books planned to be released each year. Check **musicmotivation**.com for new books, CD, singles, and more.

visit *musicmotivation.com* to purchase, or visit your local music store - Chesbro music is the national distributor for all Music Motivation® books. Contact Chesbro Music Co. if you are a store (1.800.243.7276)

Learn more about
JERALD SIMON

Visit **http://musicmotivation.com/jeraldsimon**

"My purpose and mission in life is to motivate myself and others through my music and writing, to help others find their purpose and mission in life, and to teach values and encourage everyone everywhere to do and be their best." - Jerald Simon

First and foremost, Jerald is a husband to his beautiful wife, Zanny, and a father to his wonderful children. Jerald Simon is the founder of Music Motivation® (musicmotivation.com), a company he formed to provide music instruction through workshops, giving speeches and seminars, and concerts and performances in the field of music and motivation. He is a composer, author, poet, and Music Mentor/piano teacher (primarily focusing his piano teaching on music theory, improvisation, composition, and arranging). Jerald loves spending time with his wife, Zanny, and their children. In addition, he loves music, teaching, speaking, performing, playing sports, exercising, reading, writing poetry and self help books, and gardening.

Jerald created musicmotivation.com as a resource for piano teachers, piano students, and parents of piano students. In 2008 he began creating his Cool Songs to help teach music theory – the FUN way by putting FUN back into theory FUNdamentals. Jerald has also filmed hundreds of piano lesson video tutorials on his YouTube page (youtube.com/jeraldsimon). He is the author/poet of "The As If Principle" (motivational poetry), and the books "Perceptions, Parables, and Pointers", "Motivation in a Minute", and "Who Are You?". Jerald is also the author of 21 music books from the Music Motivation® Series and has also recorded and produced several albums and singles of original music.

Jerald also presents to various music schools, groups, and associations throughout the country doing various workshops, music camps, master classes, concerts and firesides to inspire and motivate teens, adults, music students and teachers. He enjoys teaching piano students about music theory, improvisation, and composition. He refers to himself as a Music Mentor and encourages music students to get motivated by music and to motivate others through music of their own.

SPECIALTIES:

Composer, Author, Poet, Music Mentor, Piano Teacher (jazz, music theory, improvisation, composition, arranging, etc.), Motivational Speaker, and life coach. Visit **http://musicmotivation.com**, to book Jerald as a speaker/performer. Visit **http://musicmotivation.com** to print off FREE piano resources for piano teachers and piano students.

Book me to speak/perform for your group or for a concert or performance:

jeraldsimon@musicmotivation.com - (801)644-0540 - musicmotivation.com

Made in the USA
Las Vegas, NV
23 June 2022

50639210R00046